Picture Perfect

Senior Authors

Roger C. Farr

Dorothy S. Strickland

Authors

Richard F. Abrahamson ♦ Alma Flor Ada ♦ Barbara Bowen Coulter

Bernice E. Cullinan ♦ Margaret A. Gallego

W. Dorsey Hammond

Nancy Roser ♦ Junko Yokota ♦ Hallie Kay Yopp

Senior Consultant

Asa G. Hilliard III

Consultants

Lee Bennett Hopkins ♦ Stephen Krashen ♦ David A. Monti ♦ Rosalia Salinas

Harcourt Brace & Company

Orlando Atlanta Austin Boston San Francisco Chicago Dallas New York Toronto London

Requests for permission to make copies of any part of the work should be mailed to: School Permissions, Harcourt Brace & Company, 6277 Sea Harbor Drive, Orlando, Florida 32887-6777.

HARCOURT BRACE and Quill Design is a registered trademark of Harcourt Brace & Company.

Acknowledgments appear in the back of this work.

Printed in the United States of America

ISBN 0-15-310627-1

4 5 6 7 8 9 10   048   2000 99

Dear Reader,

There's a big world full of many new people and animals for you to meet. Hurry! Turn the pages of **Picture Perfect.** Say hello to friends who laugh, cry, dance, and sing just like you.

Sincerely,

The Authors

The Authors

What Can I Discover?

What Can I Discover?

What do you see in your world?
What do you like to do? You will meet many
kinds of people and animals in the stories you
will read. Some of them are just like you!

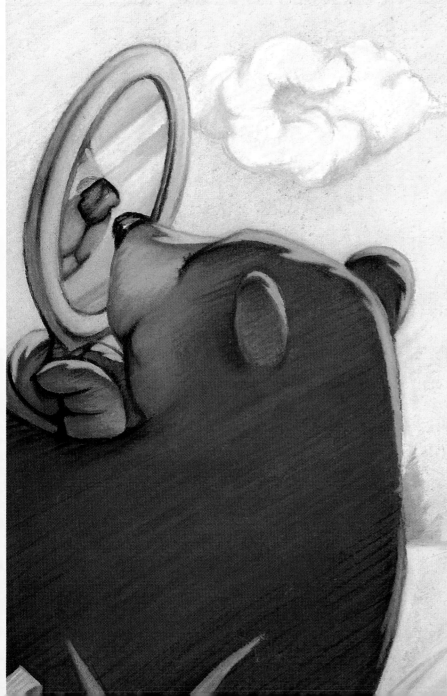

# CONTENTS

7

Bookshelf

Ten Cats Have Hats
by Jean Marzollo

A child meets a bear on a chair and two ducks with trucks. Who will be next?

Award-Winning Author
SIGNATURES LIBRARY

I Am Six
by Ann Morris

Children enjoy a day at their school.

Award-Winning Author
SIGNATURES LIBRARY

Cat on the Mat
by Brian Wildsmith

What will the cat say to the animals on the mat?

Award-Winning Author/Illustrator

Good Morning, Good Night
by Michael Grejniec

A boy and a girl find lots of things to do before the day turns into night.

What

I See

by

Holly Keller

I see a rose.

I see a nose.

I see a fly.

I see a pie.

I see a cat.

I see a mat.

I see a top.

I see a mop.

I see a dog.

I see a frog.

I see a bee.

I see me!

Holly Keller

Dear Boys and Girls,

When I am home, I love to go on walks around the pond. I thought of my walks when I wrote "What I See," because I see so many things. I know every squirrel that lives by me.

Just for fun, I hid some things in the pictures of "What I See." Can you find them? What do *you* see?

Your friend,

Holly Keller

REFLECTION

In the mirror
I can see
Lots of things
But mostly—me.

by Myra Cohn Livingston

mask

spider

two horses

RESPONSE CORNER

What Do You See?

Make a shape with paint.

You will need:

 drawing paper paint  brushes

1 Fold the paper.

2 Put paint on one side.

3 Close the paper. Press.

BLUE BUTTERFLY

What do you see? Ask some friends what they see.

Down on

by
Rita
Lascaro

DOWN ON THE FARM
WRITTEN & ILLUSTRATED
BY RITA LASCARO

the Farm

I see my dog play.

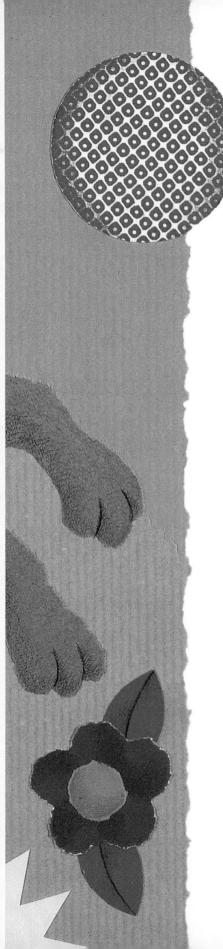

I can play like my dog.

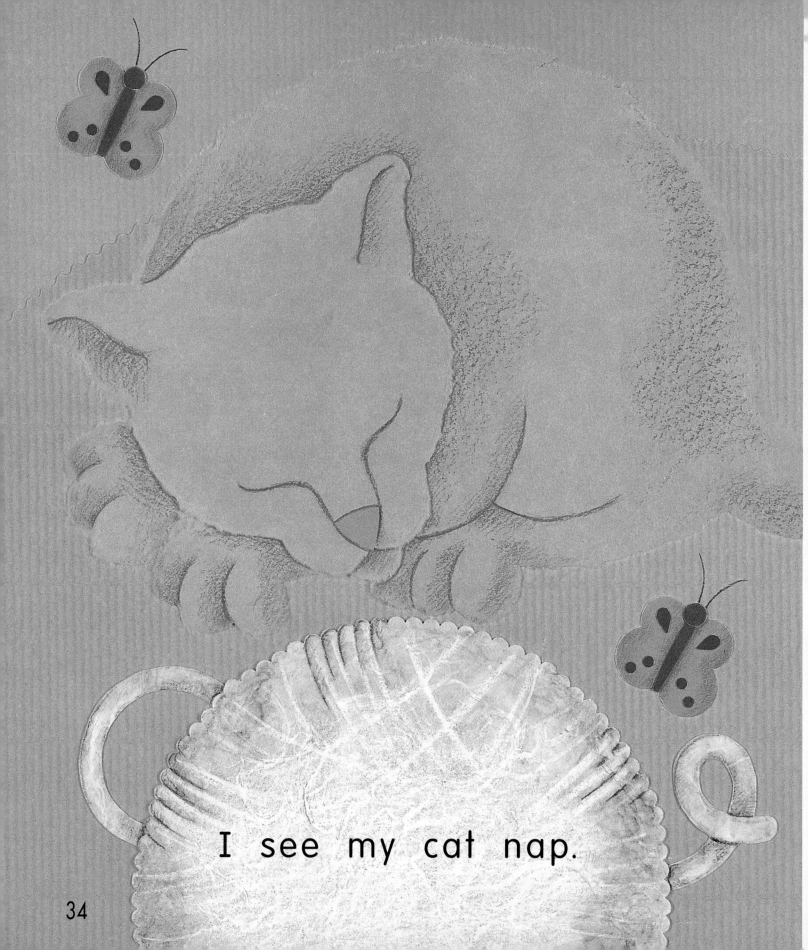

I see my cat nap.

I can nap like my cat.

I see my hen flap.

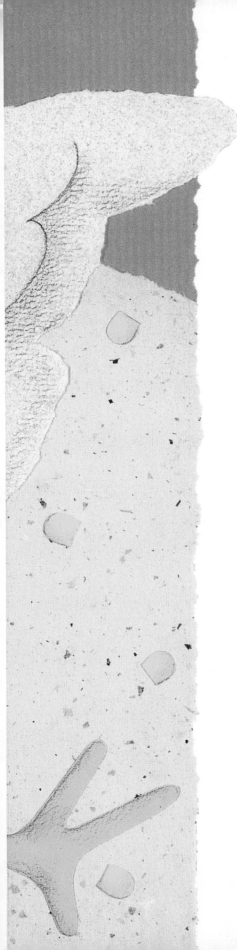

I can flap like my hen.

I see my duck swim.

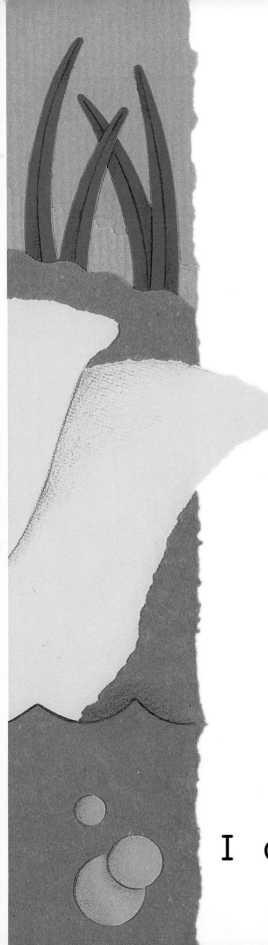

I can swim like my duck.

I see my friends ride.

I can ride like my friends...

down on the farm.

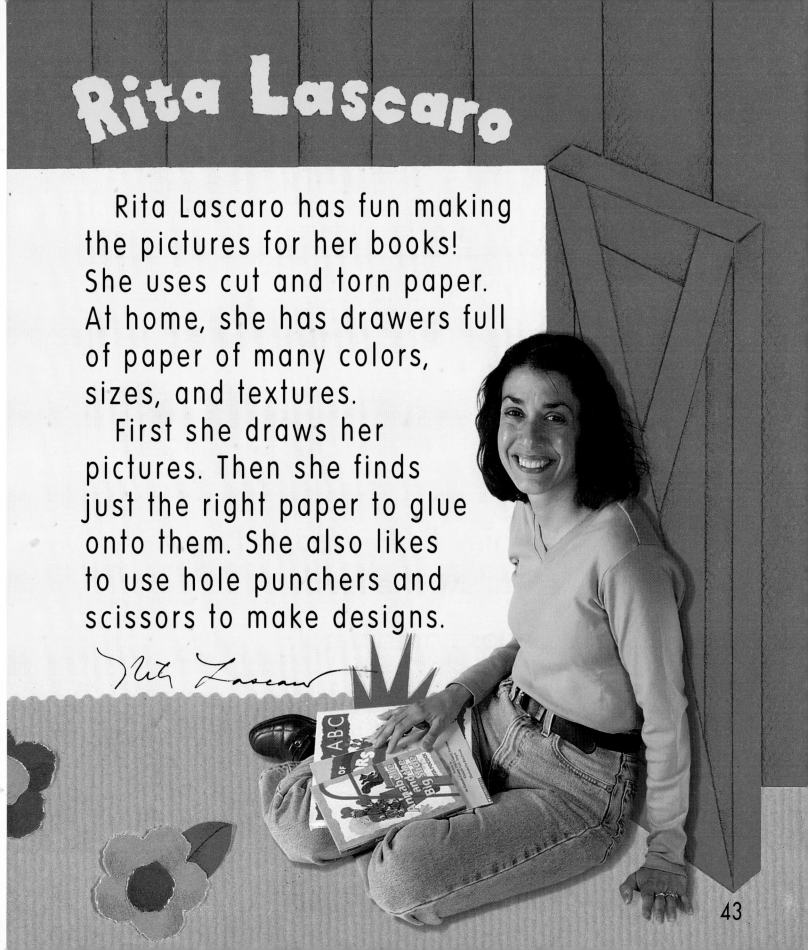

Rita Lascaro

Rita Lascaro has fun making the pictures for her books! She uses cut and torn paper. At home, she has drawers full of paper of many colors, sizes, and textures.

First she draws her pictures. Then she finds just the right paper to glue onto them. She also likes to use hole punchers and scissors to make designs.

Rita Lascaro

FOLLOW THE ANIMALS

Think of an animal. How does it move? Play animal follow-the-leader.

1. Choose an animal.
2. Draw it.
3. Be the leader.
   - Show your picture.
   - Say the rhyme and move like your animal.

A little duck went out to play.
     Back and forth it moved this way.
Come along and follow me,
     A little duck is what you'll be!

45

Sometimes

by
Keith Baker

Sometimes I am happy.

Sometimes I am not.

I like who I am.

I like what I do.

Sometimes I am hot.

Sometimes I am cold.

I like who I am.

I like what I do.

Sometimes I am up.

Sometimes I am down.

I like who I am.

I like what I do.

Sometimes I am red.

Sometimes I am blue.

I'm all of these things.
What about you?

Meet Keith Baker

Dear Boys and Girls,

My favorite color is green because I was born on St. Patrick's Day. When I was a boy, I loved to swim and ride my bike—just like the alligator in the story!

I still like to swim and ride my bike. I also like to work in my garden and cook. And, of course, I like to draw and paint. I really do like what I do!

Your friend,

Keith Baker

Mask Yourself

Do you sometimes wish to be different? Who or what would you like to be? Make a mask to show your classmates.

64

You will need:
- paper plate
- construction paper
- scissors
- glue
- crayons or markers
- craft stick
- tape

Hold the mask in front of your face. Act like the character on your mask.

65

Award-Winning
Illustrator

FIVE
LITTLE
RABBITS

66

FIVE LITTLE RABBITS

by Kristi T. Butler

illustrated by Gerald McDermott

68

Five little rabbits jumping on a mat.

One jumped off and he just sat.

Four little rabbits jumping on a mat.

One jumped off and he just sat.

Three little rabbits jumping on a mat.

One jumped off and he just sat.

Two little rabbits jumping on a mat.

One jumped off and he just sat.

One little rabbit jumping on a mat.

He jumped off and he just sat.

No little rabbits jumping on a mat.

Five little rabbits all just sat.

What did the rabbits see on the mat?

One tan hat—and one big cat!

GERALD McDERMOTT

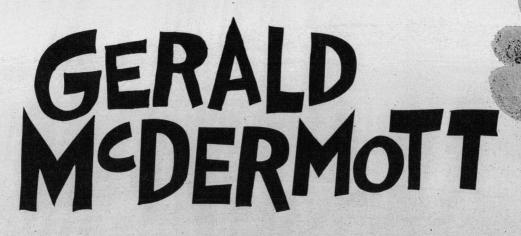

As a young boy, Gerald McDermott drew little pictures along the sides of the pages in the phone book. When he flipped the pages quickly, he could see his very own cartoon!

Gerald McDermott thought about his book *Zomo the Rabbit,* when he made the pictures for "Five Little Rabbits." He used the same kinds of bright colors to make the rabbits.

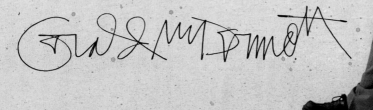

FIVE LITTLE FINGER PUPPETS

Make rabbit finger puppets!
Then use them to act out "Five Little Rabbits."

You will need:

crayons • glue • construction paper • tape • scissors

Cut strips of paper.

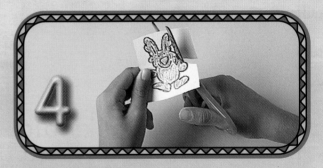

Roll each strip. Tape it.

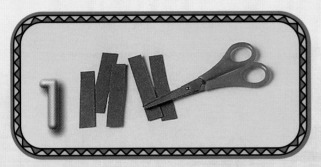

Draw five rabbits.

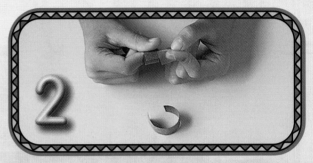

Cut them out.
Glue one to each strip.

Wear the finger puppets. Read the story. Take a puppet off your finger each time a rabbit jumps off the mat.

Baby Rabbits

Newborn

One week old

Two weeks old

Three weeks old

Four weeks old

Five weeks old

Six weeks old

I Went Walking

Sue Williams

Julie Vivas

I Went

Walking

WRITTEN BY
Sue Williams

ILLUSTRATED BY
Julie Vivas

I went walking.

What did you see?

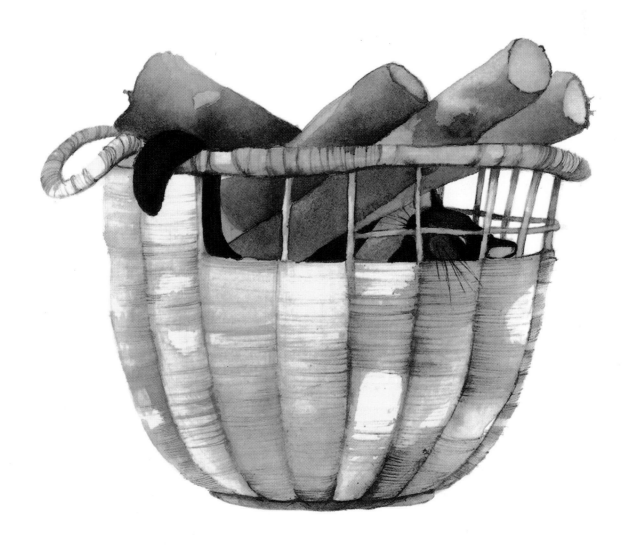

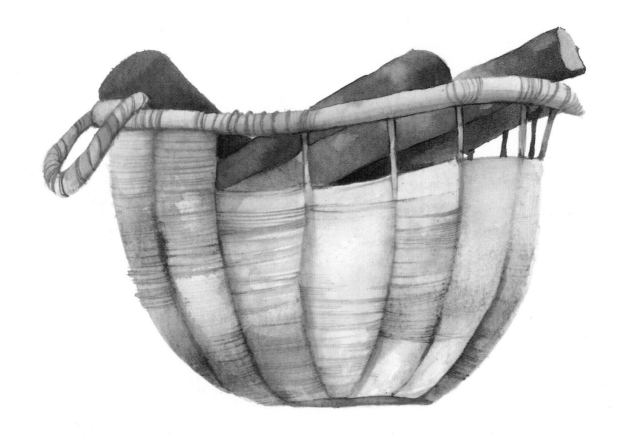

I saw a black cat
Looking at me.

I went walking.

What did you see?

I saw a brown horse
Looking at me.

I went walking.

What did you see?

I saw a red cow
Looking at me.

I went walking.

What did you see?

I saw a green duck
Looking at me.

I went walking.

What did you see?

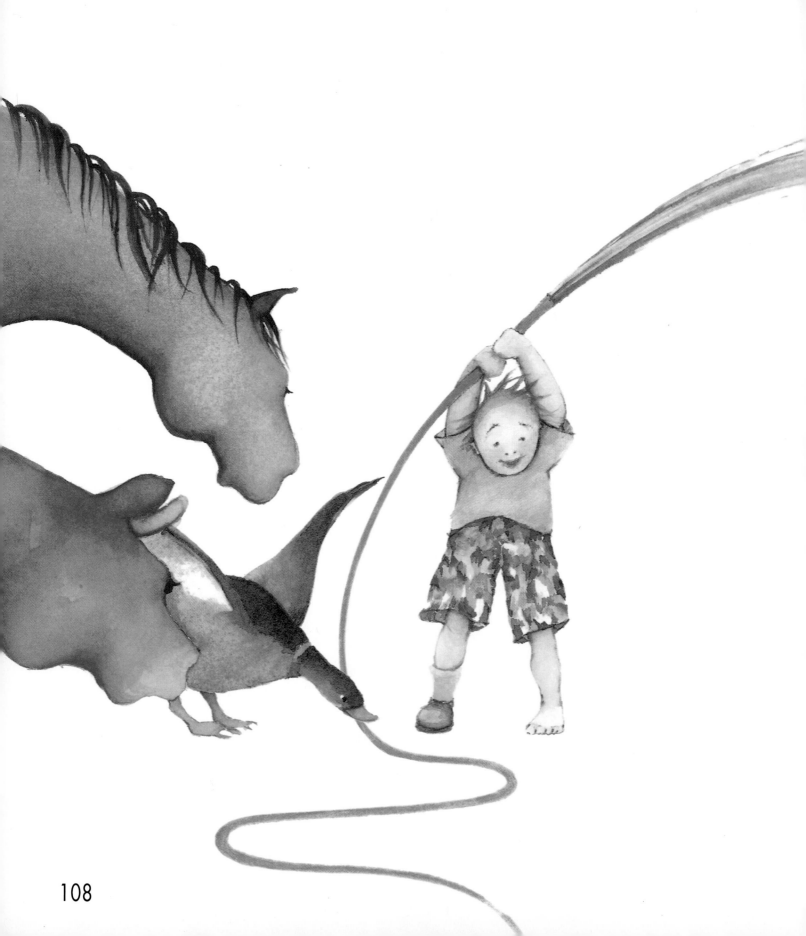

I saw a pink pig
Looking at me.

I went walking.

What did you see?

I saw a yellow dog
Looking at me.

I went walking.

What did you see?

116

I saw a lot of animals
Following me!

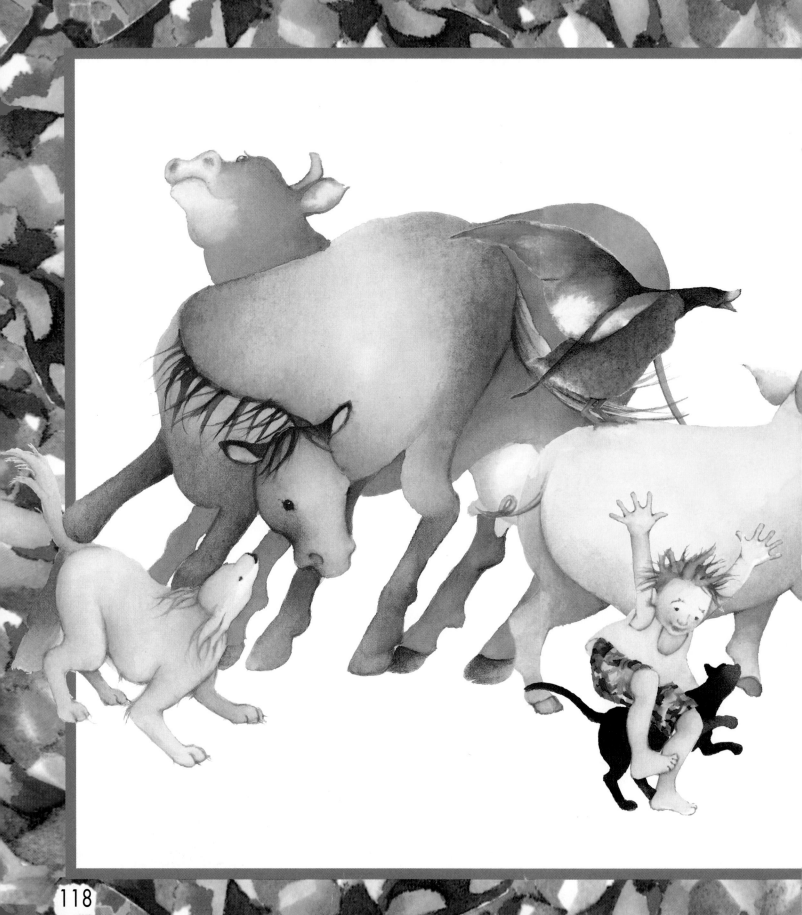

Sue Williams

Sue Williams wrote *I Went Walking* for her nieces and nephews. It is her first picture book. She lives on a farm in Adelaide, Australia, where she grows apples and raises sheep.

Julie Vivas

Julie Vivas was born in Adelaide, Australia. When she makes pictures for books, she first uses a pencil to draw the characters. As she draws, she gets new ideas and changes the pictures until they are just the way she wants them to be.

Color Memory Game

The animals in the story are different colors. Make a color game with a partner. Then play it!

You will need:
- eight index cards
- construction paper squares
- glue

Make the game.
Glue a square on each card.
Make two cards for each color.

Play the game.

1 Take turns. Turn over two cards.

2 If the colors match, keep the cards.
If not, turn them back over.

3 Then teach your game to someone else.

Quack, quack.

This is a duck.

What Do

Moo-o-o-o.

This is a cow.

Hee-haw, hee-haw.

This is a donkey.

They Say?

Gobble, gobble.

This is a turkey.

Award-Winning
Illustrator

POPCORN

Written by Alex Moran · Illustrated by Betsy Everitt

by Alex Moran

124

illustrated by Betsy Everitt

Popcorn. Popcorn.

126

Put it in a pot.

Popcorn. Popcorn.

Get the pot hot.

Popcorn. Popcorn.
Put in lots more.

Popcorn. Popcorn.
One, two, three, four.

Popcorn. Popcorn.
Pop! Pop! Pop!

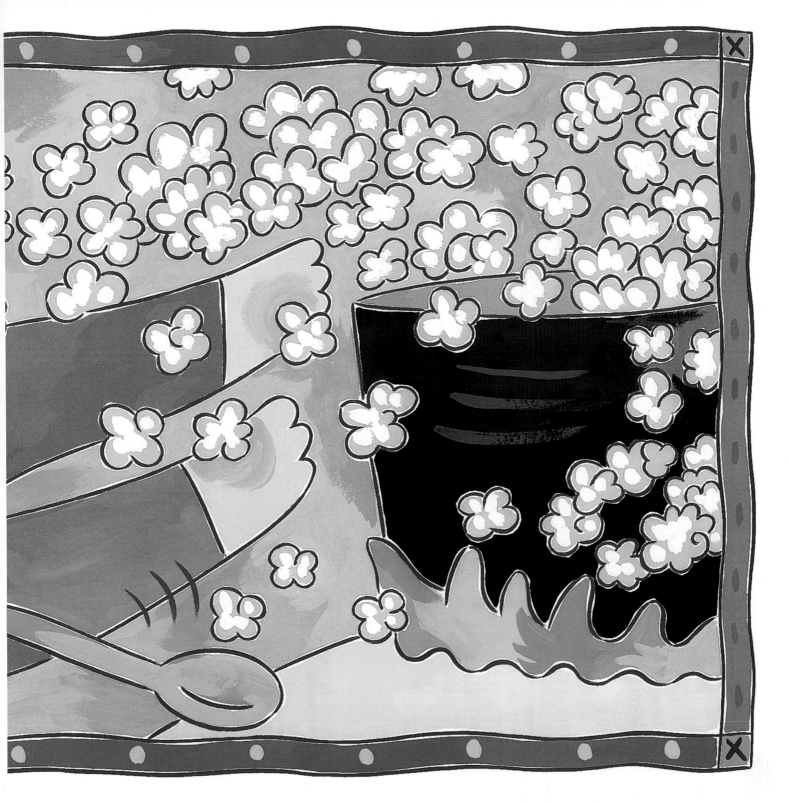

Popcorn. Popcorn.
Stop! Stop! Stop!

Popcorn. Popcorn.
What is the plan?

Popcorn. Popcorn.
Catch it if you can!

Popcorn. Popcorn.
It's going out the door.

Popcorn. Popcorn.
Stop! No more!

Popcorn. Popcorn.
Get it while it's hot.

We are happy.
We like it a lot!

BETSY EVERITT

Betsy Everitt likes to go to the movies and get a big bucket of popcorn. She and her family like to make popcorn at home, too.

Betsy Everitt chose animals with nice shapes and used lots of bright colors for this story. She put the colors and shapes together to create feelings. How do you feel when you look at her pictures?

For the Birds!

There is so much popcorn!
Why not share it with the birds?

You will need:

wire popcorn dried fruit

1 Shape the wire into a circle.

2 Put popcorn and fruit on the wire.

3 Twist the ends together.

4 Hang your wreath outside.

142

Watch for birds to come.
Keep a class journal of the birds that come.
Draw pictures of the birds you see.

Acknowledgments

For permission to reprint copyrighted material, grateful acknowledgment is made to the following sources:

Greenwillow Books, a division of William Morrow & Company, Inc.: Cover illustration from *I Am Angela* by Holly Keller. Copyright © 1997 by Holly Keller. Cover illustration from *Merry Christmas, Geraldine* by Holly Keller. Copyright © 1997 by Holly Keller. Cover illustration from *Grandfather's Dream* by Holly Keller. Copyright © 1994 by Holly Keller. Cover illustration from *Horace* by Holly Keller. Copyright © 1991 by Holly Keller.

Harcourt Brace & Company: Cover illustration by Rita Pocock from *A Jewish Holiday ABC* by Malka Drucker. Illustration copyright © 1992 by Rita Pocock. Cover illustration from *Frida the Wondercat* by Betsy Everitt. Copyright © 1990 by Betsy Everitt. Cover illustration from *Mean Soup* by Betsy Everitt. Copyright © 1992 by Betsy Everitt. Cover illustration from *TV Dinner* by Betsy Everitt. Copyright © 1994 by Betsy Everitt. Cover illustration by Betsy Everitt from *The Happy Hippopotami* by Bill Martin Jr. Illustration copyright © 1991 by Betsy Everitt. Cover illustration from *Coyote* by Gerald McDermott. Copyright © 1994 by Gerald McDermott. Cover illustration from *Raven* by Gerald McDermott. Copyright © 1993 by Gerald McDermott. Cover illustration from *Zomo the Rabbit* by Gerald McDermott. Copyright © 1992 by Gerald McDermott. Cover illustration from *Annabelle and the Big Slide* by Rita Pocock. Copyright © 1989 by Rita Pocock. *I Went Walking* by Sue Williams, illustrated by Julie Vivas. Text copyright © 1989 by Sue Williams; illustrations copyright © 1989 by Julie Vivas.

Lodestar Books, an affiliate of Dutton Children's Books, a division of Penguin Books USA Inc.: From *See How They Grow: Rabbit* (Retitled: "Baby Rabbits") by Angela Royston, photographs by Barrie Watts. Text copyright © 1991 by Dorling Kindersley Limited, London; photographs copyright © 1991 by Barrie Watts.

National Wildlife Federation: "What do they say?" from *Your Big Backyard* Magazine, July 1996. Text copyright 1996 by the National Wildlife Federation.

North-South Books Inc., New York: Cover illustration from *Good Morning, Good Night* by Michael Grejniec. Copyright © 1993 by Michael Grejniec.

Oxford University Press: Cover illustration from *Cat on the Mat* by Brian Wildsmith. © 1982 by Brian Wildsmith.

Marian Reiner: "Reflection" from *Wide Awake and Other Poems* by Myra Cohn Livingston. Text copyright © 1959 by Myra Cohn Livingston; text © renewed 1988.

Scholastic Inc.: Cover illustration by Rita Pocock from *The Land of Many Colors* by the Klamath County YMCA Family Preschool, Klamath Falls, Oregon. Illustration copyright © 1993 by Rita Pocock.

Grade 1-1

Photo Credits

Key: (t)=top, (b)=bottom, (c)=center, (l)=left, (r)=right.

Pages 28, 29, 44, 45, 64, 65, 84, 85, 120, 121, 142, 143, Campos Photography.

Page 25, Tom Sobolik / Black Star / Harcourt Brace & Co.; 28 (tl), Comstock; 28(tr), FPG; 28(bl), Lewin / The Image Bank; 28(bc), James Levin / FPG; 28(br), Stephen Marks / The Image Bank; 29, O'Brien / Mauritius / H. Armstrong Roberts; 41, Walt Chrynwski / Black Star / Harcourt Brace & Co.; 63, Joseph Rupp / Black Star / Harcourt Brace & Co.; 83, Keith Skelton / Black Star / Harcourt Brace & Co.; 86-87, Barrie Watts; 119, courtesy, Harcourt Brace & Co.; 122(t), John Shaw; 122(b), Peter Cade / Tony Stone Images; 123(t), Lynn Stone; 123(b), Jack Daniels / Tony Stone Images; 141, Dale Higgins/Harcourt Brace & Co.

Illustration Credits

Keith Baker, Cover art; Doug Bowles, 4-9; Holly Keller, 10-25; Julia Gorton, 26-27; Rita Lascaro, 30-43; Keith Baker, 46-63; Gerald McDermott, 66-83; Julie Vivas, 88-119; Betsy Everitt, 124-141.